a MILLION brilliant

Poems

(part one)

the best children's
poetry today

chosen by
Roger
Stevens

A & C Black · London

30131 04849016 0

LONDON BOROUGH OF BARNET

For Lily, Ruby, Merlin and Sam

First published 2010 by
A & C Black Publishers Ltd
36 Soho Square, London, W1D 3QY

www.acblack.com

Collection copyright © 2010 Roger Stevens
Illustrations copyright © 2010 Jessie Ford

The rights of Roger Stevens and Jessie Ford to be identified as the
editor and illustrator of this work have been asserted by them in
accordance with the Copyrights, Designs and Patents Act 1988.

ISBN 978-1-4081-2394-2

A CIP catalogue for this book is available from the British Library.

All rights reserved. No part of this publication may be reproduced
in any form or by any means – graphic, electronic or mechanical,
including photocopying, recording, taping or information storage
and retrieval systems – without the prior permission in
writing of the publishers.

This book is produced using paper that is made from wood grown in
managed, sustainable forests. It is natural, renewable and recyclable.
The logging and manufacturing processes conform to the
environmental regulations of the country of origin.

Printed and bound in Great Britain
by J F Print Ltd., Sparkford, Somerset.

Contents

January Poem

Flake on flake
the snow
rewrites the garden.

Word on word
the poem
settles on the page.

Catherine Benson

Snow Petrels

On skies and seas
veiled white with light,
snow petrels weave
and wheel in flight,

they glide and skim
from high to low,
a falling flock
of feathered snow.

In courtship chases
pair by pair
they braid their paths
of freezing air,

birds of Antarctic
paradise;
the cliffs, the sea,
the snow, the ice.

Liz Brownlee

A Date with Spring

Got a date with Spring
Got to look me best.
Of all the trees
I'll be the smartest dressed.
Perfumed breeze
behind me ear.
Pollen accessories
all in place.
Raindrop moisturiser
for me face.
Sunlight tints
to spruce up the hair.
What's the good of being a tree
if you can't flaunt your beauty?
Winter, I was naked.
Exposed as can be.
Me wardrobe took off
with the wind.
Life was a frosty slumber.
Now, Spring, here I come.
Can't wait to slip in
to me little green number.

John Agard

Jemima

Running down the garden path
Jemima, seven years old
Lifts her eyes to watch the sun
Drown in clouds of gold.
Sees her old friend smiling down
Through the chestnut tree
Her face among the branches smiles
White as ivory.
Jemima tells her secrets
Her breath is like a sigh
Wishing on a star that falls
Dying through the sky.
Jemima up the evening path
Through twilight bright as noon
Tells anyone who'll listen,
'I've been talking to the moon.'

Gareth Owen

Low Owl

Cold morn: on fork of two o'clock
Owl's hoot flows from hood to wood.
Owl's song rolls from blood to brood,
Owl's hoot loops on to top of town roofs,
Owl's song swoops on strong doors.
Owl's slow whoop – long, forlorn –
Soft flood of moon song.

John Rice

Solo Flight

Looks like a long, long, long way down
to the ground.
Sounds
like a long, long, long way down
to the ground.
Something says
I'm sure to be safe,
because I'm a baby bat,
but,
but,
but I think I'll hang around
for an itsy-bitsy bat-bit longer.
No!
Why, mum, why?
Time flies
and so must I...
Well, if you say so,
first time solo,
here I go.   I can
fly!
Here I go.   I can fly.
   Here I go   I can fly.
                 o   o

           o   o

              o

Mike Johnson

Batty About Bats

I'm batty about
bats.
I'm head-over-heels in love with
somersaults.
Encores leave me crying out for
more.
I think that flying insects' joints are the bee's
knees,
and that Oxygen is a
gas...
But ice cubes leave me
c-c-cold.

Philip Ardagh

I Like to Stay Up

I like to stay up
and listen
when big people talking
jumbie stories
I does feel
so tingly and excited
inside me
But when my mother say
'Girl, time for bed'
This is when
I does feel a dread
This is when
I does jump into me bed
This is when
I does cover up
from me feet to me head

Then is when
I does wish I didn't listen
to no stupid jumbie story
This is when
I does wish I did read
me book instead

Grace Nichols

Jumbie is a Guyanese word for ghost

I Know What It Was

They said it was just
an owl in the tree
but they didn't
fool me!

I saw teeth
not a beak,
red eyes
not gold,
and I won't be told
it was only
a fluff of feathers
round its throat;
it was a collar
and those weren't wings
but the silky folds
of a black, black cloak.

That was no
Too-wit, too-woo
I heard.
It was
I'll get yoo-ou!

    Patricia Leighton

A Poem to Be Spoken Silently

It was so silent that I heard
my thoughts rustle
like leaves in a paper bag...

It was so peaceful that I heard
the trees ease off
their coats of bark...

It was so still that I heard
the paving stones groan
as they muscled for space...

It was so silent that I heard
a page of this book
whisper to its neighbour,
'Look, he's peering at us again...'

It was so still that I felt
a raindrop grin
as it tickled the window's pane...

It was so calm that I sensed
a smile crack the face
of a stranger...

It was so quiet that I heard
the morning earth roll over
in its sleep and doze
for five minutes more...

Pie Corbett

The Dark

Why are we so afraid of the dark?
It doesn't bite and it doesn't bark
Or chase old ladies round the park
Or steal your sweeties for a lark

And though it might not let you see
It lets you have some privacy
And gives you time to go to sleep
Provides a place to hide or weep

It cannot help but be around
When beastly things make beastly sounds
When back doors slam and windows creek
When cats have fights and voices shriek

The dark is cosy, still and calm
And never does you any harm
In the loft, below the sink
It's somewhere nice and quiet to think

Deep in cupboards, pockets too
It's always lurking out of view
Why won't it come out till it's night?
Perhaps the dark's afraid of light

James Carter

Small Dawn Song

This is just to say Thank You

to the tick
  of the downstairs clock
    like a blind man's stick
      tap-tip on through the dark

to the lone
  silly blackbird who sang
    before dawn when no one
      should have been listening

to the wheeze
  and chink of the milk float
    like an old nightwatchman clinking keys
      and clearing his throat

          Six o'clock and all's well
          Six o'clock and all's well

The night's been going on
                        so long
                        so long
This is just to say Thank You

  Philip Gross

A Potato Clock

A potato clock, a potato clock
Has anyone got a potato clock?
A potato clock, a potato clock
Oh where can I find a potato clock?

I went down to London the other day
Found myself a job with a lot of pay
Carrying bricks on a building site
From early in the morning till late at night

No one here works as hard as me
I never even break for a cup of tea
My only weakness, my only crime
Is that I can never get to work on time

A potato clock, a potato clock
Has anyone got a potato clock?
A potato clock, a potato clock
Oh where can I find a potato clock?

I arrived this morning half an hour late
The foreman came up in a terrible state
'You've got a good job, but you're in for
   a shock
If you don't get up at eight o'clock.'

Up at eight o'clock, up at eight o'clock
Has anybody got up at eight o'clock?
Up at eight o'clock, up at eight o'clock
Oh where can I find up at eight o'clock?

Roger McGough

Last Night, I Saw the City Breathing

Last night, I saw the city breathing.
Great gusts of people,
Rushing in and
Puffing out
Of stations' singing mouths.

Last night, I saw the city laughing.
Takeaways got the giggles,
Cinemas split their sides,
And living rooms completely creased
   themselves!

Last night, I saw the city dancing.
Shadows were cheek to cheek with brick
   walls,
Trains wiggled their hips all over the place,
And the trees
In the breeze
Put on a show for an audience of windows!

Last night, I saw the city starving.
Snaking avenue smacked her lips
And swallowed seven roundabouts!
Fat office blocks got stuffed with light
And gloated over empty parking lots.

Last night, I saw the city crying.
Cracked windows poured falling stars
And the streets were paved with mirrors.

Last night, I saw the city sleeping.
Roads night-dreamed,
Streetlamps quietly boasted,
'When I grow up, I'm going to be a star!'

And the wind,
Like a cat,
Snoozed in the nooks of roofs.

Andrew Fusek Peters

A Crack Band

Early morning boiler gives a bagpipe bellow,
starts to heat the water, makes it chuckle like
   a cello,

radiators wake up with a tinging and a ping –
pizzicato plucking of a violin,

metal's making music on a xylophone,
pipes are groaning notes like an old trombone,

castanets are clacking, there's a clanging from
   a gong
as the house warms up and the band plays on.

Gina Douthwaite

In the Time of the Wolf

Who sings the legend?
The mouse in the rafters,
the owl in the forest,
the wind in the mountains,
the tumbling river.

Where can we read it?
In a shadow on the grass,
in the footprint in the sand,
in reflections on the water,
in the fossil in the stone.

How shall we keep it?
In the lake of history,
in the box called memory,
in the voice of the teller,
in the ear of the child.

How will we tell it?
With a tongue of lightning,
with a drum of thunder,
with a strumming of grasses,
with a whisper of wind.

Gillian Clarke

Roots

It's a quiet job
being a root.
No one hugs you,
climbs you
or praises your
intricate ways.

Roots work
in the dark.
And it's hard work
tunnelling,
travelling,
finding nutrition.

But when
the storms come
it's our fingers
which cling.
When the drought comes
it's our lips
that drink.

Without us
the ground would crumble.
Without us
life would fall.

Everyone
needs roots.

Steve Turner

Plum

Don't be so glum,
plum.

Don't feel beaten.

You were made
to be eaten.

But don't you know
that deep within,
beneath your juicy flesh
and flimsy skin,

you bear a mystery,
you hold a key,

you have the making of
a whole new tree.

Tony Mitton

Just a Skin Thing

This is the skin
That I've grown up in.
I've filled every part
And look pretty smart.
It starts at my head,
Reaches down to my feet,
It stretches so I can
Sit down on a seat.
It's got a few freckles
That others can see,
And fingerprint markings
To prove that I'm me.
Skin comes in all sizes
And colours and shades,
And proves, without doubt,
We're all brilliantly made!

Coral Rumble

28

Dressing Up

When I dress up
I always feel
just like a queen
in Mum's high heels.

I want to look
my queenly best,
so I'll put on
Mum's new long dress.

Crown jewels next.
Now, let me see,
where does Mum keep
her jewellery?

On royal lips,
the queen then slicks
a nice thick layer
of Mum's lipstick.

Uh oh! Here's Mum,
I fear the worst.
The queen forgot
to ask Mum first.

Jane Clarke

Nought to Nine

A ring made of gold, a doughnut and hole,
something that's nothing that's easy to roll.

A periscope raised, a walking stick,
the cut of a cake and a candle's new wick.

A swan on a lake,
a nun knelt in prayer,
an FA Cup handle raised in the air.

The pout of a mouth,
a bird flying over,
a bra on a line,
two leaves of a clover.

A neatly pressed ribbon,
a kite without string,
the nose of a witch
and an arm in a sling.

The hand of a pirate, a flat-headed snake,
an apple divided, the latch on a gate.

A teardrop to wipe, a cherry and stalk,
the speech mark to use when your words
    start to talk.

Half a triangle, a fox's ear tip,
an arrow, an arm of a hand on a hip.

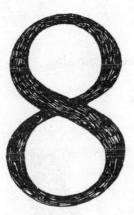

Balancing balls
and a circular kiss,
a hoop with a waist and
a rope in a twist.

A hook in a curtain, chameleon's tongue,
the whistle to blow when this poem is done.

Rachel Rooney

Body Talk

Dere's a Sonnet
Under me bonnet
Dere's a Epic
In me ear,
Dere's a Novel
In me navel
There's a Classic
Here somewhere.
Dere's a Movie
In me left knee
A long story
In me right,
Dere's a shorty
Inbetweeny
It is tickly
In de night.
Dere's a picture
In me ticker
Unmixed riddims
In me heart,
In me texture
Dere's a comma
In me fat chin
Dere is Art.
Dere's an Opera
In me bladder
A Ballad's in me wrist
Dere is laughter
In me shoulder
In me guzzard's

A nice twist.
In me dreadlocks
Dere is syntax
A dance kicks
In me bum
Thru me blood tracks
Dere run true facts
I got limericks
From me Mum,
Documentaries
In me entries
Plays on history
In me fold,
Dere's a Trilogy
When I tink of three
On me toey
Dere's a joke.

Benjamin Zephaniah

Mr Khan's Shop

is dark and beautiful.
There are parathas,

garam masala,
nan breads full of fruit.

There are bhajees, samosas, dhal,
garlic, ground cumin seeds.

Shiny emerald chillies
lie like incendiary bombs.

There are bhindi in sacks,
aloo to eat with hot puris

and mango pickle. There's
rice, yoghurt,

cucumber and mint –
raita to cool the tongue.

Sometimes you see
where the shop darkens

Mr Khan, his wife
and their children

round the table.
The smells have come alive.

He serves me
poppadums, smiles,

re-enters the dark.
Perhaps one day

he'll ask me to dine with them:
bhajees, samosas, pakoras,

coriander dhal.
I'll give him this poem: *Sit down,*

young man, he'll say
and eat your words.

   Fred Sedgwick

If I Were a Shape

If I were a shape
I'd be a rectangle
I'd be a snooker table with Steve Davies
    potting the black
I'd be a football pitch where Spurs would
    always be winning,
I'd be a chocolate bar that you could never
    finish
If I were a rectangle.

If I were a circle,
I'd be a hoop rolling down a mountainside,
I'd be a wheel on a fast Ferrari
I'd be a porthole in Captain Nemo's
    submarine
If I were a circle.

If I were a cone
I'd be a black hat on a witch's head,
I'd be a warning to motorists, one of
    thousands,
I'd be a tooth in a T. rex's jaw,
If I were a cone.

But if I were a star...
I'd be Robbie Williams.

Brian Moses

In the Bath

When I pull the plug out
with my round and
wrinkly toe,
the water
likes
to
g
u
r
g
l
e
as
it
d
i
s
a
p
p
e
a
r
s
b
e
l
o
w

Andrew Collette

The Can-can

When I dance
my blood runs like a river can,
my feet fly like the birds can,
my heart beats like a drum can.
Because when I dance I can,
can do anything
when I dance.

Flying over rooftops
I see my town below me
where everybody knows me,
where all my problems throw me,
where heavy feet can slow me.
But nobody can, can stop me
when I dance.

My blood runs a race.
My feet fly in space.
My heart beats the pace.
Because when I dance I can,
can do anything
when I dance.

Mandy Coe

All About Poets

A poet is for life
not just for Christmas Day.
Stroking a silky-haired poet
can soothe your troubles away.

A long-haired breed of poet
Should always be kept well-groomed.
Keep their sleeping quarters
in a draught-free part of the room.

Do not indulge your poet
with titbits from your plate.
Encourage regular exercise
to avoid excessive weight.

It is generally thought unhealthy
to have poets in your bed.
Be sensitive about disposal
once your poet is dead.

Sorry, I meant to say 'pet'.

Trevor Parsons

The Cat and the Pig

Once, when I wasn't very big
I made a song about a pig
    who ate a fig
    and wore a wig
and nimbly danced the Irish jig.

And when I was as small as THAT
I made a verse about a cat
    who ate a rat
    and wore a hat
and sat (you've guessed) upon the mat.

    And that, I thought, was that.

But yesterday upon my door
I heard a knock; I looked and saw
    a hatted cat
    a wiggèd pig
    who chewed a rat
    who danced the jig
    on my doormat!

They looked at me with faces wise
out of their bright enquiring eyes,
'May we come in? For we are yours,
pray do not leave us out of doors.
We are the children of your mind
let us come in. Be kind. Be kind.'

So now upon my fireside mat
there lies a tireless pussy cat
who all day long chews on a rat
        and wears a hat.
And round him like a whirligig
dancing a frantic Irish jig
munching a fig, cavorts a big
        wig-headed pig.

They eat my cakes and drink my tea.
There's hardly anything for me!
And yet I cannot throw them out
for they are mine without a doubt.

But when I'm at my desk tonight
I'll be more careful what I write.

Gerard Benson

The Dark Avenger

My dog is called The Dark Avenger
Hello, I'm Cuddles
She understands every word I say
Woof?
Last night I took her for a walk
Woof! Walkies! Let's go!
Cleverly, she kept three paces ahead
I dragged him along behind me
She paused at every danger, spying out the land
I stopped at every lamppost
When the coast was clear, she sped on
I slipped my lead and ran away
Scenting danger, Avenger investigated
I found some fresh chip papers in the bushes
I followed, every sense alert
*He blundered through the trees, shouting 'Oy, come
    'ere! Where are you?'*
Something – maybe a sixth sense – told me to
    stop
He tripped over me in the dark
There was a pale menacing figure ahead of us
Then I saw the white Scottie from next door
Avenger sprang into battle, eager to defend her
    master
Never could stand terriers
They fought like tigers
We scrapped like dogs
Until the enemy was defeated
Till Scottie's owner pulled him off – spoilsport!

Avenger gave a victory salute
I rolled in the puddles
And came to check I was all right
I shook mud over him
'Stop it, you stupid dog!'
He congratulated me
Sometimes, even The Dark Avenger can go
    too far.
Woof!

Trevor Millum

I Do As Simon Says

I'm nobody's dog but Simon's
I do as Simon says,
If Simon says, Delilah, dance!
I'd be up on my two hind legs.

But Simon says, Delilah, sit!
He says, Delilah, stay!
Yet if he said, Delilah, sing!
I'd somehow find a way.

I'm nobody's dog but Simon's
I do as Simon says,
He sometimes says, Delilah, fetch!
And I save Simon's legs.

But Simon is no tyrant,
He takes me out for walks.
I always keep one step ahead
And listen as he talks.

My watchword is Obedience,
And Simon's love, my prize;
We go together everywhere
For I am Simon's eyes.

Celia Warren

Gift

Flat, under the mat
Like a pressed violet
In a lady's book
There is a vole.
Its body curled like a flower
Its tail a thin, thin stem.
It is my gift to you
And you will hate it
Almost as much as I think it
   wonderful.

That's because you are stupid
And I am a cat.

   Jan Dean

Grandma Was Eaten by a Shark

Grandma was eaten by a shark
Dad, by a killer whale
And my baby brother got slurped up
By a rather hungry sea snail
A cuttlefish cut my mum to bits
An octopus strangled my sister
A jellyfish stung my auntie's toes
Giving her terrible blisters
A pufferfish poisoned my grandpa
A dogfish ate my cat
And then a catfish ate my dog!
I was very upset about that
So go for a swim if you like
Just don't ask me to come too
I'm staying here with my camera
I can't wait to see what gets you!

Andrea Shavick

An Elephant Is Born

Night holds them safe,
the cloud moon gleams,
in the darkness
of soft breath and dreams,

the elephant mother
greets her new son,
with a tender and gentle
low, soft hum,

she strokes his face
the night-left long,
and sings her newborn
elephant song.

Liz Brownlee

Rhinoceros

God simply got bored and started doodling
with ideas he'd given up on, scooping off the
   floor
bits and bobs and sticking them together:
the tail of a ten-ton pig he'd meant for
   Norway,
the long skull of a too-heavy dinosaur
the armour plating of his first version of
the hippo, an unpainted beak of a toucan
stuck on back to front, a dash of tantrums
he intended for the Abyssinian Owl, the same
awful grey colour he's used for landscaping
   the moon.
And tempted to try it with the batteries,
he set it down on the wild plains of Africa,
grinned at what he saw and let it run.

Matt Simpson

Emergencies

Red Alert! Red Alert!
I've dropped my lolly in the dirt.

S.O.S! S.O.S!
I've spilled some custard
down my dress.

999! 999!
My bike's got tangled
in the washing line.

Ring the alarm! Ring the alarm!
There's an insect landing on my arm.

Bring First Aid! Bring First Aid!
There's a beetle in my lemonade.

Ambulance! And make it quick!
I think I'm going to be sick.

Tony Mitton

The Great Escape

In the Great Escape from London Zoo
eight caribou and gnu they knew
mounted a minor military coup,
an act of animal derring-do,
and locked the staff they overthrew
in the 'potamus pit and a portaloo,
then caught a plane to North Peru.
As animals broke out two-by-two
to squeal and growl and grunt and moo
a loud unruly queue soon grew
that wriggled and ran and crawled and flew,
stampeding down the avenue.

In the Great Escape from London Zoo
we heard how a herd of kangaroo
had bid the big brown owl adieu
with a 'Toodle-oo, mate, toodle-oo!'
but before he'd time to twit-tu-woo
they'd hopped it, heading for Timbuktu
and the owl himself had flown off too.
While a crocodile and a cockatoo
crossed the Thames in a slim canoe
rowed by the bird, so the croc could chew ...
chew through the bones of the eight-man crew
till the river ran red instead of blue.

In the Great Escape from London Zoo
the pandas abandoned their bamboo
and all dressed up as railway crew

hijacked the fifteen fifty-two
from platform three at Waterloo
and 'parley-voo' they zoomed straight through
Paris, and on to Kathmandu.
Panic ensued and ballyhoo
when pot-bellied pig and rare-breed ewe
gatecrashed a very posh barbecue
terribly upsetting the well-to-do
and causing a heck of a hullabaloo.

You doubt my word? What's wrong with you?
Why, every detail here is true.
The Great Escape from London Zoo.
When was that? I thought you knew:
Years ago, at half-past two.

Nick Toczek

Ten Things Found in a Shipwrecked Sailor's Pocket

A litre of sea.
An unhappy jellyfish.
A small piece of a lifeboat.
A pencil wrapped around with seaweed.
A soaking feather.
The first page of a book called *Swimming Is Easy*.
A folded chart showing dangerous rocks.
A photograph of a little girl in a red dress.
A gold coin.

A letter from a mermaid.

Ian McMillan

Riddles of the Seashore

Tossed into tangles by waves
it drizzles salt-sparkle onto sand.

Soft under seaweed the toe-nipper
waits for new armour.

Pentagram on the beach
fish with a sky-name.

Not for collecting or poking,
leave this jellymould body for the tide.

In a bowl of barnacled rock a tiny sea
covers sea-flowers, shrimps and a crab.

Written in the sand, a seagull's poem
is rubbed out by the waves.

As far as the eye can see, scallops
of white embroidery on grey-blue and
    blue-green.

Holding secret sea-songs and carried home,
It spills music into my ear.

Catherine Benson

A Liking for the Viking

I've always had a liking for the Viking;
His handsome horns; his rough and ready
    ways;
His rugged russet hair beneath his helmet
In those metal-rattle, battle-happy days.

I've always had a longing for a longboat;
To fly like a dragon through the sea
To peaceful evenings round a real fire,
Alive with legend; rich with poetry.

I've always had a yearning for the burning
Of brave flames irradiating valour;
For the fiery longboat carrying its chieftain
To his final feast in glorious Valhalla.

Celia Warren

The Emergensea

The octopus awoke one morning and
   wondered what rhyme it was.
Looking at his alarm-clocktopus
he saw that it had stopped
and it was time to stop having a rest
and get himself dressed.
On every octofoot
he put
an octosocktopus
but in his hurry, one foot got put
not into an octosock
but into an electric plug socket
and the octopus got a nasty electric
   shocktopus
and had to call in the octodoctopus
who couldn't get in
to give any help or medicine
because the door was locktopus.
The octopus couldn't move, being in a state
   of octoshocktopus
so the octodoctopus bashed the door
   to the floor
and the cure was as simple as could be:
a nice refreshing cup of
seawater.

John Hegley

Shouting at the Ocean

Last week the sea was whispering,
hushing and shushing the beach,
sifting its salty secrets into the sand.

But this evening the moon is full
and the sea's found its voice; it bellows and
   roars,
sings aloud, booms in the Smugglers' Cave.

And me? I'm shouting right back at it,
shouting at the ocean. Full voiced.
I fill my lungs and let go.

I call out my name over and over,
then other words. Roller! Smash! Crash!
Wow! Boulder! Ocean! Ocean! Ocean!

The wind comes whistling and lifts my words
and carries them over the waves.
Wow! Roller! Ocean! Ocean! Ocean!

Gerard Benson

Little Barbara

Little Barbara went to Scarborough,
Just to buy a candelabra.
At the harbour a bear ate Barbara.
Don't you find that most macabre?

Colin West

Python Poem

I slither round my tank of glass,
I crush the tufts of plastic grass,
I watch the scaly minutes pass
And grow, Grow, GROW.

I see another dawn begin,
I shed my tight and tattered skin,
I smile my wide and hungry grin
And grow, Grow, GROW.

My world is small but I am king,
I glitter like a jewelled ring,
I gulp a small and feathered thing
And grow, Grow, GROW.

Human slaves, beware, beware!
Approach my castle if you dare,
And watch your little ones with care
I GROW, GROW, GROW!!!

Clare Bevan

Juggling with Gerbils

Don't juggle with a gerbil
No matter what the thrill
For gerbils when they're juggled
Can end up feeling ill.
It makes them all bad-tempered
And then they'd like to kill
Those gerbil-juggling jugglers
Juggling gerbils till they're ill

Brian Patten

Question Time

What does a monster look like?

Well ... hairy and scary
And furry and burly and pimply and dimply
    and warty
and ... naughty.
That's what a monster looks like.

How does a monster move?

It oozes
It shambles
It crawls and it ambles
It slouches and shuffles and trudges
It lumbers and waddles
It tiptoes and toddles.
That's how a monster moves.

Where does a monster live?

In garden sheds
Under beds
In wardrobes
In plug holes
In ditches
Beneath city streets
Just under your feet.
That's where a monster lives.

How does a monster eat?

It slurps
And it burps
It gobbles and gulps
It sips and it swallows
And scoffs.
It nibbles
And munches
It chews
And it crunches.
That's how a monster eats!

WHAT does a monster eat?

Slugs
And bats
And bugs
And rats and stones
And mud
And bones and blood
And squelchy squids ...

... and nosy kids.
That's what a monster eats.

YUM!

Michaela Morgan

Monster Boast

He's as big as a gorilla
but he fits into my hand,
his skin is made of metal
and his blood is made of sand.

He can breathe underwater
though he'd rather breathe air
and he grants me special wishes
which he keeps in his hair.

He doesn't like the darkness
even though he CAN see
and he doesn't like broccoli
(just like me).

He can walk on the ceiling
AND he can fly,
he's got a door in his stomach
that serves gognacious pie.

It's him that you should blame for
eating chocolates off the tree
and hiding all the wrappers
under the settee.

He isn't being naughty –
it's just the way he's made;
he ONLY eats chocolate
and he drinks lemonade.

You'd like to meet my monster?
I'm afraid he's very shy.
He gets invisibility
when grown-ups pass by.

I'll show you his tooth marks, though,
here, on my bed,
the ones that look like felt-tip, yes,
his teeth are blue and red.

Oh, and he's got antlers
AND he's magnetic...
his hands are made of comic books
AND... Oh, forget it!

Ros Barber

Aunty Ruby

Aunty Ruby had a dinosaur
She took it everywhere
She taught it how to knit and sew
And wash her underwear

She used to ride upon its nose
A great mistake, I think
'Cause it sneezed her into outer space
And now Aunty is extinct

Sue Hardy-Dawson

Word of a Lie

I am the fastest runner in my school and that's
NO WORD OF A LIE

I've got gold fillings in my teeth and that's
NO WORD OF A LIE

In my garden, I've got my own big bull
and that's
NO WORD OF A LIE

I'm brilliant at giving my enemies grief
and that's
NO WORD OF A LIE

I can multiply three billion and twenty-seven
by nine billion four thousand and one in two
seconds and that's
NO WORD OF A LIE

I can calculate the distance between the planets
before you've had toast and that's
NO WORD OF A LIE

I can always tell when my best pals boast
and that's
NO WORD OF A LIE

I'd been round the world twice before I was three
and a quarter and that's
NO WORD OF A LIE

I am definitely my mother's favourite daughter
and that's
NO WORD OF A LIE

I am brilliant at fake laughter. I go Ha aha Ha ha
Ha and that's
NO WORD OF A LIE

I can tell the weather from one look at the sky
and that's
NO WORD OF A LIE

I can predict disasters, floods, earthquakes and
murders and that's
NO WORD OF A LIE

I can always tell when other people lie
and that's
NO WORD OF A LIE

I can even tell if someone is going to die
and that's
NO WORD OF A LIE

I am the most popular girl in my entire school
and that's
NO WORD OF A LIE

I know the golden rule: don't play the fool, don't
boast, be shy and that's
NO WORD OF A LIE

I am sensitive, I listen, I have kind brown eyes
    and that's
NO WORD OF A LIE

You don't believe me, do you?
ALL RIGHT, ALL RIGHT, ALL RIGHT
I am the biggest liar in my school and that's
NO WORD OF A LIE

Jackie Kay

Absent

Dear Teacher,
my body's arrived
it sits at a table
a pen in its hand
as if it is able
to think and to act
perhaps write down the answer
to the question you've asked

but don't let that fool you.

My mind is elsewhere.
My thoughts far away.

So apologies, teacher,
I'm not here today.

Bernard Young

No Feel for Numbers

In English
I'm a livewire!
Ideas
Whizz
Fizz
Crackle from my brain
Like fireworks at a display.
Words
Zap
Snap
Sizzle
From my pen
Like sparks from a white-hot electrode!

But in maths
My thoughts become static
(My hair stands on end!)
And as the minutes drag by
My brain gets
Number
And
Number
And
Number
And
Number...

Philip Waddell

Mister Moore

Mister Moore, Mister Moore
Creaking down the corridor

Uh uh eh eh uh
Uh uh eh eh uh

Mister Moore wears wooden suits
Mister Moore's got great big boots
Mister Moore's got hair like a brush
And Mister Moore don't like me much

Mister Moore, Mister Moore
Creaking down the corridor

Uh uh eh eh uh
Uh uh eh eh uh

When my teacher's there I haven't got a care
I can do my sums, I can do gerzinters
When Mister Moore comes through the door
Got a wooden head filled with splinters

Mister Moore, Mister Moore
Creaking down the corridor

Uh uh eh eh uh
Uh uh eh eh uh

Mister Moore, I implore
My earholes ache, my head is sore

Don't come through that classroom door.
Don't come through that classroom door.

Mister Moore, Mister Moore
Creaking down the corridor

Uh uh eh eh uh
Uh uh eh eh uh

Big voice, big hands
Big feet, he's a very big man
Take my advice, be good, be very, very nice
Be good, be very, very nice
To Mister Moore, Mister Moore
Creaking down the corridor

Uh uh eh eh uh
Uh uh eh eh uh

Mister Moore wears wooden suits
Mister Moore's got great big boots
Mister Moore's got hair like a brush
And Mister Moore don't like me much

Mister Moore, Mister Moore
Creaking down the corridor

Uh uh eh eh uh
Uh uh eh eh uh

David Harmer

Corrections

Teacher said,
Leave out the the,
two too's one too too many
and and after the comma
should go after the any.

The the, the too –
and move the and
and that should make it flow.
Not that that, that that's fine –
but this that, that could go.

I said,
The the, the too, the and –
I would agree with you.
But I'm very fond of that –
this that and that that too.

Which that is that?
Is that this that?
Asked teacher with a grin.
Okay – but take that last in out
And leave that last out in.

Roger Stevens

The Painting Lesson

'What's THAT, dear?'
asked the new teacher.

'It's Mummy,' I replied.

'But mums aren't green and orange!
You really haven't TRIED.
You don't just paint in SPLODGES
You're old enough to know
You need to THINK before you work...
Now – have another go.'

She helped me draw two arms and legs,
A face with sickly smile,
A rounded body, dark brown hair,
A hat – and, in a while,
She stood back (with her face bright pink):
'That's SO much better – don't you think?'

But she turned white
At ten to three
When an orange-green blob
Collected me.

'Hi, Mum!'

Trevor Harvey

I Think I'm the
Only One

I think I'm the only one
who closes my eyes for the prayers in assembly
but I can't be sure ...
because I think I'm the only one
who closes my eyes for the prayers in assembly.

Paul Cookson

Just Doing My Job

I'm one of Herod's Henchmen.
We don't have much to say,
We just charge through the audience
In a Henchman sort of way.

We all wear woolly helmets
To hide our hair and ears,
And wellingtons sprayed silver
To match our tinfoil spears.

Our swords are made of cardboard
So blood will not be spilled
If we trip and stab a parent
When the hall's completely filled.

We don't look VERY scary,
We're mostly small and shy,
And some of us wear glasses,
But we give the thing a try.

We whisper Henchman noises
While Herod hunts for strangers,
And then we all charge out again
Like nervous Power Rangers.

Yet when the play is over
And Miss is out of breath
We'll charge like Henchmen through the hall
And scare our mums to death.

Clare Bevan

Retiring

Our teacher, Mrs Batlow
is leaving this week,
after 40 years of teaching.
So on Friday all of Class 5W
give her a present.
Most of us give her a card
with 'best wishes' but
Sarah presents her with a painting,
of Mrs Batlow standing in front of the school.
Emily gives her some flowers.
Nathan gives her a box of chocolates.
Lorenzo gives her a framed photo of
    Class 5W.
Penny gives her a box of apples!
(Penny's dad owns a fruit shop.)
Simon gives her a pen in a special case.
Mrs Batlow smiles at each present
And thanks every child
But when Peter gives her his homework
all finished, neat and tidy,
for the first time this year
we all notice that
Mrs Batlow is crying
but
we're not sure if she's happy
or
if she's crying because
she has to mark Peter's homework.

Steven Herrick

Whatshisname

That chap who wrote lots of plays...
His name's on the tip of my tongue:
Wobbledart? Waggledagger?
Swaysticker? Joggleprong?
Shuddershaft? Quiverlance? Wavespike?
Not quite, but I'm getting near...
It's something like Jigglejavelin...
I've got it! His name's Shakespeare!

Eric Finney

Pupil Troubles

There once was a teacher, Miss Wright,
Whose lessons affected her sight.
Through all of her classes
She sported dark glasses –
Her students were simply *too bright!*

Graham Denton

My Spectacular Adventure

I have just returned from
That strange
And dangerous world
Called:
The Other Side of Dave's Glasses
Where
pavements rear up at your face
stairs fall away into space
and pointy-headed aliens
catch your bus to school.
Where
lampposts dance in a mist
while cars swirl and twist
and your bus ticket
begins to unspool.
Where
the flies are the size of mice
and blurry girls look quite nice
and walls wobble
like ripples in a pool.
Where
a scaly, tentacled thing
opens a crocodile mouth to sing
'You've got my specs on
upside down, you fool!'

John Coldwell

Aliens Stole My Underpants

To understand the ways
of alien beings is hard,
and I've never worked it out –
why they landed in my backyard.

And I've always wondered why
on their journey from the stars,
these aliens stole my underpants
and took them back to Mars.

They came on a Monday night
when the weekend wash had been done,
pegged out on the line
to be dried by the morning sun.

Mrs Driver from next door
was a witness at the scene
when aliens snatched my underpants –
I'm glad that they were clean!

It seems they were quite choosy
as nothing else was taken.
Do aliens wear underpants
or were they just mistaken?

I think I have a theory
as to what they wanted them for,
they needed to block off a draught
blowing in through the spacecraft door.

Or maybe some Mars museum
wanted items brought back from space.
Just think, my pair of Y-fronts
displayed in their own glass case.

And on the label beneath
would be written where they got 'em
and how such funny underwear
once covered an Earthling's bottom!

Brian Moses

World of Weird

In the world of Weird
all the girls wear beards
and the boys keep bees in their beds
the girls dig holes and live like moles
and the boys grow trees on their heads

In the world of Weird
all the oranges are blue
and the lemons are as sweet as can be
bananas are round, and grow in the ground
or down at the bottom of the sea

In the world of Weird
all the fish can fly
and the chips are fried in lakes
the dogs love cats – with sauce, of course,
served up on silver plates

Now how do you get
to the world of Weird?
where is it? where is it? where?
hop on a bee – pop over the sea
then give us a call when you're there!

James Carter

Late Worker

Dad works on the night shift
he goes alone into the dark

He has no supper. Mum says
he gets a bite at work

but he tells us a story, tucks us in
and slips away like a shadow into shadows

He's always back by daybreak,
his long black coat hangs in the hall

but his sad eyes, his great weariness
show how tiring the work must be

and why else would he need to sleep all day
in a wooden box in a cold cellar?

Dave Calder

My Mum's Put Me on the Transfer List

On Offer:
One nippy striker, ten years old
Has scored seven goals this season
Has nifty footwork and a big smile
Knows how to dive in the penalty box
Can get filthy and muddy within two minutes
Guaranteed to wreck his kit each week
This is a FREE TRANSFER
But he comes with running expenses
Weeks of washing shirts and shorts
Socks and vests, a pair of trainers
Needs to scoff huge amounts
Of chips and burgers, beans and apples
Pop and cola, crisps and oranges
Endless packets of chewing gum.
This offer open until the end of the season
I'll have him back then;
At least until the cricket starts.
Any takers?

David Harmer

I Luv Me Mudder

I luv me mudder an me mudder luvs me
   We cum so far from over de sea
We heard dat de streets were paved wid gold
   Sometimes it's hot, sometimes it's cold,
I luv me mudder and me mudder luvs me
   We try fe live in harmony
Yu might know her as Valerie
   But to me she's just my mummy.

She shouts at me daddy so loud sometime
   She's always been a friend of mine
She's always doing de best she can
   She works so hard down ina Englan,
She's always singin sum kinda song
   She has big muscles an she very, very
   strong,
She likes pussycats an she luvs cashew nuts
   She don't bother wid no if an buts.

I luv me mudder an me mudder luvs me
   We come so far over de sea
We heard dat de streets were paved wid gold
   Sometimes it's hot, sometimes it's cold,
I luv her and whatever we do
   Dis is a luv I know is true,
My people, I'm talking to yu
   Me an me mudder we luv yu too.

Benjamin Zephaniah

Dad, Don't Dance

Whatever you do, don't dance, Dad
Whatever you do, don't dance
Don't wave your arms
Like a crazy buffoon
Displaying your charms
By the light of the moon
Trying to romance
A lady baboon
Whatever you do, don't dance

When you try to dance
Your left leg retreats
And your right leg starts to advance
Whatever you do, don't dance, Dad
Has a ferret crawled into your pants?
Or maybe a hill full of ants
Don't samba
Don't rumba
You'll tumble
And stumble
Whatever you do, Dad, don't dance

Don't glide up the aisle with the trolley
Or twirl the girl on the till
You've been banned from dancing in Tesco
'Cos your tango made everyone ill
Whatever you do, don't dance, Dad
Whatever you do, don't dance

Don't make that weird face
Like you ate a sour plum
Don't waggle your hips
And stick out your bum
But most of all – PLEASE –
Don't smooch with Mum!
Whatever the circumstance
Whatever you do –
Dad, don't dance

Roger Stevens

Guidance

Wash yuh han' dem before yuh eat,
Sit still, teck yuh foot dem off the seat,
Don' scrape the plate with yuh knife an' fork,
An' keep quiet when big people a-talk
Stop drag yuh foot dem pon the floor,
Ah tell yuh a'ready, don' slam the door,
Cover up yuh mout' when yuh a-cough,
Don' be greedy, give yuh sister half
O' the banana that yuh eatin' there,
What kind o'dress that yuh a-wear?
Don' kiss yuh teeth when me talk to yuh,
An' mind how yuh lookin' at me too,
Teck me good advice, me girl,
Manners carry yuh through the worl',
Ah tellin' yuh this fe yuh own good,
Yuh should thank me, show some gratitude.

Life is very tough for me,
When Uncle Henry comes to tea.

   Valerie Bloom

Uncle and Auntie

My auntie gives me a colouring book and
   crayons
I begin to colour
after a while Auntie leans over and says
you've gone over the lines
what do you think they're for
eh?
some kind of statement is it?
going to be a rebel are we?
your auntie gives you a lovely present
and you have to go and ruin it
I begin to cry
my uncle gives me a hanky and some blank
   paper
do some doggies of your own he says
I begin to colour
when I have done
he looks over
and says they are all very good
he is lying
only some of them are

John Hegley

Who Started It?

When me and my brother have a fight
My mum says:
'Stoppit – someone'll get hurt.'

And we say:
'He started it.'
'I didn't. He started it.'

I say:
'Mum, who started the very first fight
between me and Brian?'

And she says:
'You.'

'Me? But I'm four years younger than him.
How could it have been me?'

And she says:
'Well, it was like this...
You were about two years old
and Brian was six.
You were sitting in your high chair
eating your breakfast
and Brian walked past.
You leaned forward
and banged him over the head
with your spoon.'

'There you are,' says my brother,
'you started it,
you started it.
I always knew you started it.'

Michael Rosen

Peter

I'm not sitting next to Peter
For he's such a messy eater,
And although he's my own brother
Can't we swap him for another?
(For I'd so prefer a sibling
Who is not forever dribbling.)

Colin West

Actions Speak

He never said a word, my brother,
Just brought me a tissue – or two –
A cup of tea, chocolate biscuits
And his copy of *The Beano*.

Left them on my bedside table,
Squeezed my shoulder, smiled
And left me alone for a while.

Never said a word.
Never had to.
Knew just how I felt.

Paul Cookson

When Granny

Song-bird shut dem mout' an lissen
Church bell don' bother to ring,
All de little stream keep quiet
When mi granny sing.
De sun up in de sky get jealous,
Him wish him got her style,
For de whole place full o' brightness
When mi granny smile.
First a happy soun' jus' bubblin'
From her belly, low an' sof',
Den a thunderclap o' merriment
When mi granny laugh.
De tree branch dem all start swingin'
Puss an' dawg begin to prance,
Everyt'ing ketch de happy fever
When mi granny dance.
All o' we look out fe Granny
Mek sure dat she satisfy,
For de whole worl' full o' sadness
When mi granny cry.

Valerie Bloom

Borrowed Time

Great-gran is ninety-six.
'I'm living on borrowed time,'
she said.

'Who did you borrow it from?'
asked my little sister.

'Never you mind,' said Gran.

'I hope you said thank you,'
said my sister.

Great-gran laughed.
'I do,' she said.
'Every single day.'

John Foster

Grandad

You've been dead two years
but your cap sits on its peg
pretending, like me.
I thought you'd come home.
Your hug in my dream last night
kept me warm all day.

Celia Gentles

A Place without Footprints

I'm searching for a place
Without footprints,
But I'm the youngest child.
Whatever I try,
Wherever I go,
Whatever I choose,
One of them has already
Succeeded,
Been there,
Chosen first.
I'm just a comparison,
Usually unfavourable.
Born to follow,
To repeat the pattern,
The footprints are never mine.
But I'll keep moving,
Hoping the direction is new,
Hoping that one day
A space *will* appear
Like a fresh snowfall,
Untouched,
Unnoticed by the others,
As I'm searching for a place
Without footprints,
As I'm searching for a place
To plant mine.

Daphne Kitching

Windows

you look out
of the window
together

you see the
dullness of rooftops
weeds in the garden
the intractable back
of the man
next door

she sees a bird
perched
on a chimney
a colourful
kaleidoscope
of flowers
and stones
and feathery grass
the shy smile
of her friend
next door.

Joan Poulson

Walk

Confetti blows
outside the church
as I walk by.
Late summer wind
is dusty, dry.
No children play
in these long streets.
I stare at sweets
locked up behind
thick glass and steel
and want to cry.
The wedding guests
are somewhere else,
like happiness.

Carol Ann Duffy

Footballers in the Park

December. Wet Saturday in the park.
It's late afternoon and it's growing dark

as a bevy of boys play their football game.
Most wear baggy shorts. One goalie's lame.

Posts are old jerseys and hand-me-down
    coats;
the boys' boots are bulky as rowing boats.

Leather ball's sodden and heavy with mud.
It thumps a boy's face with a squelchy thud

and blood dribbles down from a nose struck
    numb:
a fat lad stunningly skids on his bum.

One boy shivers in his 'Wednesday' shirt,
the collar's ripped and he's plastered with
    dirt.

The game rattles on; chill drizzle sets in.
The wind in the trees makes a Cup Final din.

Distantly, lights shine on the wet street
unnoticed by boys whose thundering feet

are playing the game. But the hour grows late.
Here comes the park keeper to padlock the
    gate.

And the year is nineteen forty-eight.

Wes Magee

Red Boots On

Way down Geneva,
All along Vine,
Deeper than the snow drift
Love's eyes shine:

Mary Lou's walking
In the winter time.

She's got

Red boots on, she's got
Red boots on,
Kicking up the winter
Till the winter's gone.

So

Go by Ontario,
Look down Main,
If you can't find Mary Lou,
Come back again:

Sweet light burning
In winter's flame.

She's got

Snow in her eyes, got
A tingle in her toes

And new red boots on
Wherever she goes

So

All around Lake Street,
Up by St Paul,
Quicker than the white wind
Love takes all:

Mary Lou's walking
In the big snow fall.

She's got

Red boots on, she's got
Red boots on,
Kicking up the winter
Till the winter's gone.

   Kit Wright

Notes Towards a Poem

Sky, grey. Late frost
Laces glass, distracts.
Trees, still. Paper, white.

Inside my head
Red lava rumbles
In an unquiet earth;
Black storm clouds gather,
Tigers poise to spring,
A yellowed river
Presses at its banks.
Ice binds nothing here
And over lightning flash
And ocean roar
The mountain bursts.
Tigers crash,
White ocean horses
Gallop in flood tide
And down the mountainside
The red-hot torrent pours.

Sky, grey. Late frost
Trees, laced glass, lost.
Paper, black on white.

   Judith Nicholls

Give Yourself a Hug

Give yourself a hug
when you feel unloved

Give yourself a hug
when people put on airs
to make you feel a bug
Give yourself a hug
when everyone seems to give you
a cold-shoulder shrug

Give yourself a hug –
a big big hug

And keep on singing,
'Only one in a million like me
Only one in a million-billion-trillion-zillion
like me.'

Grace Nichols

Index of First Lines

Acknowledgements

All poems have been included with permission of the authors.

'Absent' by Bernard Young first appeared in *Brilliant!* by Bernard Young, published by Kingston Press, 2000.

'Aliens Stole My Underpants' by Brian Moses first appeared in *Behind the Staffroom Door – the very best of Brian Moses*, published by Macmillan Children's Books, 2007.

'A Liking for the Viking' by Celia Warren first appeared in *Vikings Don't Wear Pants, Potty Poems of the Past*, edited by Roger Stevens and Celia Warren, published by The King's England Press, 2001.

'An Elephant Is Born' by Liz Brownlee first appeared in *Shouting at the Ocean, Poems That Make a Splash*, edited by Graham Denton, Roger Stevens and Andrea Shavick, published by Hands Up Books, 2009.

'A Place without Footprints' by Daphne Kitching first appeared in *I Remember, I Remember*, edited by Brian Moses, published by Macmillan Children's Books, 2003.

'A Poem to Be Spoken Silently' by Pie Corbett first appeared in *A Noisy Noise Annoys*, edited by Jennifer Curry, published by The Bodley Head, 1996.

'Borrowed Time' by John Foster first appeared in *The Poetry Chest* by John Foster, published by OUP, 2007.

'The Can-can' by Mandy Coe first appeared in *Hot Heads, Warm Hearts, Cold Streets*, edited by John Foster, published by Nelson Thornes, 1996.

'The Cat and the Pig' by Gerard Benson first appeared in *To Catch an Elephant* by Gerard Benson, published by Smith/Doorstop, 2002.

'Corrections' by Roger Stevens first appeared in *I Did Not Eat the Goldfish* by Roger Stevens, published by Macmillan Children's Books, 2002.

'Dad, Don't Dance' by Roger Stevens first appeared in *The Monster That Ate the Universe* by Roger Stevens, published by Macmillan Children's Books, 2004.

'The Dark' by James Carter first appeared in *Cars, Stars, Electric Guitars* by James Carter, published by Walker Books, 2002.

'The Dark Avenger' by Trevor Millum first appeared in *Warning – Too Much Schooling Can Damage Your Health* by Trevor Millum, published by Nelson Thornes, 1991.

'Dressing Up' by Jane Clarke first appeared in *See You Later, Escalator*, compiled by John Foster, published by OUP, 2002.

'Emergencies' by Tony Mitton, first appeared in *Pip* by Tony Mitton, published by Scholastic Press, 2002.

'Grandad' by Celia Gentles first appeared in *The Poetry Store*, compiled by Paul Cookson, published by Hodder Children's Books, 2005.

'Grandma Was Eaten by a Shark' by Andrea Shavick first appeared in *Grandma Was Eaten by a Shark!* by Andrea Shavick, published by Crocodile Books, 2002.

'The Great Escape' by Nick Toczek first appeared in *The Great Escape*, edited by Gaby Morgan, published by Macmillan Children's Books, 2000.

'A Crack Band' by Gina Douthwaite first appeared in *A Noisy Noise Annoys*, edited by Jennifer Curry, published by The Bodley Head, 1996.

'I Do As Simon Says' by Celia Warren first appeared in

Taking My Human for a Walk, chosen by Roger Stevens, published by Macmillan Children's Books, 2003.

'If I Were a Shape' by Brian Moses first appeared in *The Works 2*, edited by Brian Moses and Pie Corbett, published by Macmillan Children's Books, 2002.

'I Know What It Was' by Patricia Leighton first appeared in *Seriously Scary Poems*, edited by John Foster, published by HarperCollins, 2003.

'Juggling with Gerbils' by Brian Patten first appeared in *Juggling with Gerbils* by Brian Patten, published by Puffin, 2000.

'Just a Skin Thing' by Coral Rumble first appeared in *Breaking the Rules* by Coral Rumble, published by Lion Children's Books, 2004.

'Just Doing My Job' by Clare Bevan first appeared in *Read Me 1, A Poem for Every Day of the Year*, edited by Gaby Morgan, pubished by Macmillan Children's Books, 1998.

'Last Night I Saw the City Breathing' by Andrew Fusek Peters first appeared in *Mad, Bad and Dangerously Haddock* by Andrew Fusek Peters, published by Lion Books, 2006.

'Low Owl' by John Rice first appeared in *Bears Don't Like Bananas* by John Rice, published by Simon & Schuster, 1991.

'Monster Boast' by Ros Barber first appeared in *Monster Poems*, published by Macmillan Childrens Books, 2005.

'The Painting Lesson' by Trevor Harvey first appeared in *The Usborne Book of Funny Poems*, published by Usborne, 1990.

'Plum' by Tony Mitton, first appeared in *Plum* by Tony Mitton, published by Scholastic Press, 1998.

'Potato Clock' by Roger McGough first appeared in *Sky in*

the Pie by Roger McGough, published by Puffin, 2003, reproduced by permission of PFD on behalf of Roger McGough.

'Python' by Clare Bevan first appeared in *Taking My Human for a Walk*, edited by Roger Stevens, published by Macmillan Children's Books, 2003.

'Riddles of the Seashore' by Catherine Benson first appeared in *The Universal Vacuum Cleaner*, edited by John Foster, published by OUP, 2005.

'Roots' by Steve Turner first appeared in *I Was Only Asking*, edited by Steve Turner, published by Lion Hudson, 2004.

'Shouting at the Ocean' by Gerard Benson first appeared in *Shouting at the Ocean, Poems That Make a Splash*, edited by Graham Denton, Roger Stevens and Andrea Shavick, published by Hands Up Books, 2009.

'Small Dawn Song' by Philip Gross first appeared in *The All-Nite Café* by Philip Gross, published by Faber, 1993.

'Snow Petrels' by Liz Brownlee first appeared in *Shouting at the Ocean, Poems That Make a Splash*, edited by Graham Denton, Roger Stevens and Andrea Shavick, published by Hands Up Books, 2009.

'Whatshisname' by Eric Finney first appeared in *Shorts*, edited by Paul Cookson, published by Macmillan Children's Books, 2000.

'World of Weird' by James Carter first appeared in *Time-travelling Underpants* by James Carter, published by Macmillan Children's Books, 2007.

All efforts have been made to seek permission for copyright material, but in the event of omissions, the publisher would be pleased to hear from the copyright holders and to amend these acknowlegements in subsequent editions.